AN **I AM HEALING** SERIES

A SAFE PLACE

Strategies to Feel Better

CHRISTY LYNN ANANA

A Safe Place
Strategies to Feel Better
AN I AM HEALING SERIES BOOK
by Christy Lynn Anana

Anana Press
ISBN: 978-1-957400-01-3
Illustrations by Shiraz Buhar, @sonabuhar, Fiverr.com
Cover and Interior design by Suzanne Fyhrie Parrott

ChristyLynnAnana.com

*Printed in the
United States of America*

I see you.
I am curious:
How is it going?

Do you need some time to talk?
Do you need some time to just be?

Let's do this together.
I will be here for you.
I want you to know you're not alone.

Where do you feel this
big feeling in your body?
Your throat?
Your belly?
Your heart?
Your head?
Everywhere?

Does the feeling have a name?
That makes sense.

While keeping your head still, move your eyes to notice something on the left side of the room.

Move your eyes to notice something on the right side. Go back
and forth a few times. Now, take a big breath.

If you feel comfortable, gently close your eyes. In your mind's eye imagine a place in nature where you feel very safe. Maybe it's the beach, the lake, the mountains, the woods, or your backyard. Notice the temperature of the air, the sun, the wind.

Is there sand between your toes or dry,
crunchy leaves under your feet?
Do you hear birds or waves or forest creatures?
Do you smell salty air or pine needles or your wet dog?

Feeling so safe in this place, go ahead and walk and notice. As
you walk, there is a gentle rain shower. You feel like the rain
washes some of your worries away.

Stay here for a moment.

Then, you see a little cabin.
This place is familiar and safe.
You walk up some steps.
You see the color of the door.
You open the door and walk in.

There is a table for you to sit.
It feels so good to be here.

To help you, invite a person you trust or character from a book to offer you some advice on what to do. You listen to their good words. You see from their eyes how much this person cares and loves you.

You notice yourself feeling lighter and better.

You realize that is
time to get back.

You thank your person.

You know that you can
come to this safe place
whenever you want to.

Maybe, you'll come visit
before you sleep tonight.

You like that idea.

You see the color of the door and step into the outside.
The rain has cleared, and you see the sunshine. You smell
the scents, see the colors, and hear the sounds.

It all seems so much better and more clear.

Say your gentle goodbyes
to your nature scene

You know you can come back
to this place anytime you like.

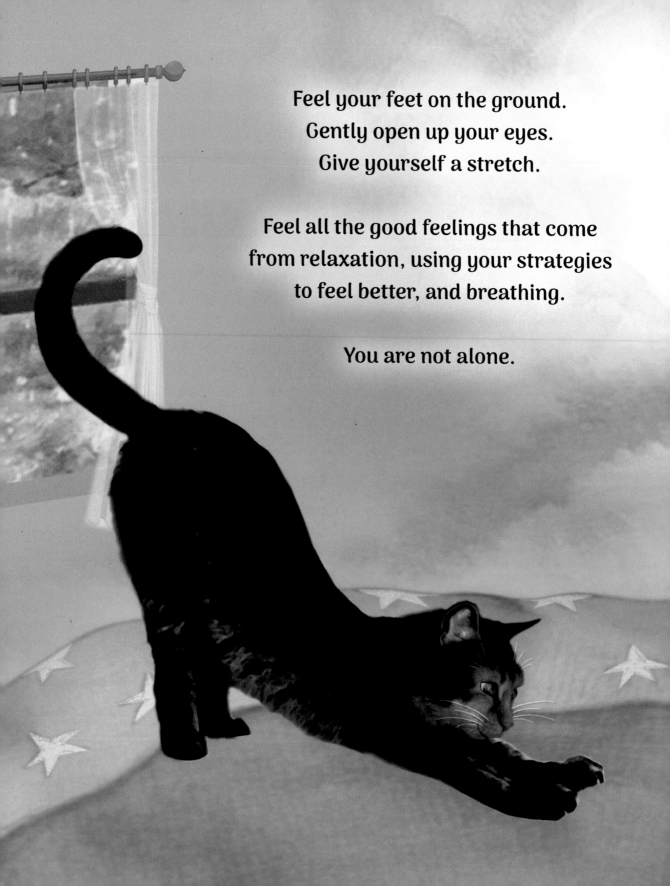

Feel your feet on the ground.
Gently open up your eyes.
Give yourself a stretch.

Feel all the good feelings that come
from relaxation, using your strategies
to feel better, and breathing.

You are not alone.

ABOUT THIS STRATEGY

- EMDR (Eye Movement Desensitization and Reprocessing) was developed by Dr. Francine Shapiro as she noticed herself feeling better while watching her windshield wipers in her car.

  Check out many resources at: EMDRIA.org.

- Safe Place is a resourcing technique to bring about a sense of calm and safety

- Resourcing is a way to install coping skills so that you are able to deal with a difficult experience so you can feel better in this moment.

Made in the USA
Middletown, DE
04 December 2023

44182506R00015